audition
songs for kids
musicals

C000154122

Wise Publications
part of The Music Sales Group
London / New York / Paris / Sydney / Copenhagen / Berlin / Madrid / Tokyo

Published by
Wise Publications
14-15 Berners Street, London W1T 3LJ, UK.

Exclusive Distributors:
Music Sales Limited
Distribution Centre, Newmarket Road,
Bury St Edmunds, Suffolk IP33 3YB, UK.
Music Sales Pty Limited
20 Resolution Drive, Caringbah, NSW 2229, Australia.

Order No. AM991463
ISBN 978-1-84772-215-7
This book © Copyright 2009 Wise Publications,
a division of Music Sales Limited.

Compiled by Nick Crispin
Edited by Fiona Bolton
Printed in the EU

CD recorded, mixed and mastered by Jonas Persson
Backing tracks arranged by Paul Honey
Keyboard by Paul Honey
Guitars by Arthur Dick
Bass by Don Richardson
Drums by Chris Baron

Your Guarantee of Quality
As publishers, we strive to produce every book to the
highest commercial standards.
This book has been carefully designed to minimise awkward
page turns and to make playing from it a real pleasure.
Particular care has been given to specifying acid-free,
neutral-sized paper made from pulps which have not been
elemental chlorine bleached. This pulp is from farmed
sustainable forests and was produced with special regard
for the environment.
Throughout, the printing and binding have been planned to
ensure a sturdy, attractive publication which should give years
of enjoyment.
If your copy fails to meet our high standards, please inform us
and we will gladly replace it.

www.musicsales.com

Breaking Free

Words & Music by Jamie Houston

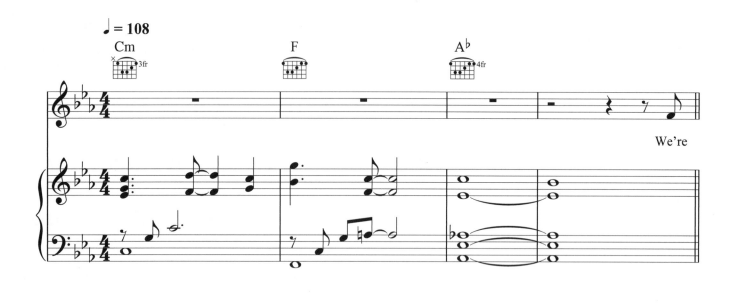

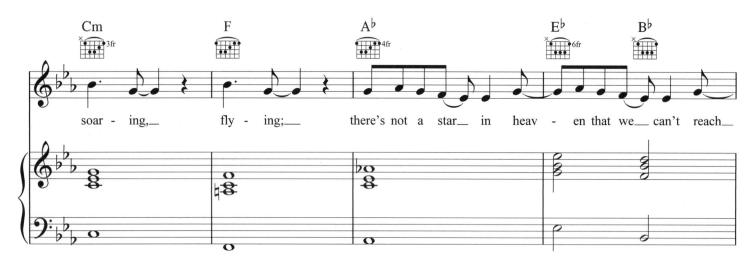

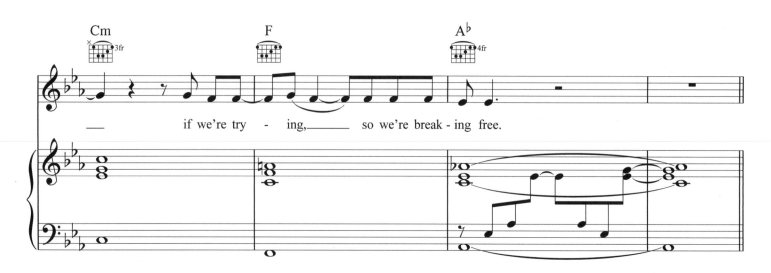

7

Castle On A Cloud

Music by Claude-Michel Schönberg
Original Lyrics by Alain Boublil & Jean-Marc Natel
English Lyrics by Herbert Kretzmer

1. There is a cas-tle on a cloud,
2. There is a room that's full of toys,

I like to go there in my sleep.
there are a hun-dred boys and girls.

Aren't an-y floors for me to
No-bod-y shouts or talks too

Chim Chim Cher-ee

Words & Music by Richard M. Sherman & Robert B. Sherman

world there's no 'ap - pi - er bloke.

Chim chim - i - ney, chim chim - i - ney, chim chim che -

-ree. A sweep is as luck - y as

luck - y can be. Chim chim - i - ney,

"Chim chim che - ree, chim che - roo." Chim chim - i - ney,

chim chim, che - ree, chim... Cheer - i - o, Bert. *Keep an eye on them for me.*

Majestically ♩ = 130

Close Every Door

Music by Andrew Lloyd Webber
Lyrics by Tim Rice

hate me and laugh at me, dark-en my day-time and tor-ture my
on-ly one per-son, de - stroy me com - plete-ly, then throw me a -

night. }
-way. }

If my life were im - por-tant I would ask will I

live or die, but I know the an-swers lie far from this world.

2. Close ev - 'ry door to me, keep those I love from me

Popular

Words & Music by Stephen Schwartlz

know I know ex - act - ly what they need! And e - ven in your case, tho' it's the

tough - est case I've yet to face,___ don't wor - ry, I'm de - ter - mined to suc -

-ceed. Fol - low my lead and yes, in - deed you will be...

Bright and bubbly

Pop - u - lar,___ You're gon - na be pop - u - lar! I'll teach_ you the

I Whistle A Happy Tune

Words by Oscar Hammerstein II
Music by Richard Rodgers

My Favourite Things

Words by Oscar Hammerstein
Music by Richard Rodgers

feel - ing sad,_____ I sim - ply re - mem - ber my

fav - our - ite things, and then I don't feel_____

so bad._____

Sandy

Words & Music by Louis St. Louis & Scott Simon

Where Is Love

Words & Music by Lionel Bart

1. Where_____ is love? Does it fall from skies a-

-bove? Is it un-der-neath the wil-low tree_____ that

You're Never Fully Dressed Without A Smile

Words by Martin Charnin
Music by Charles Strouse

CD Track Listing

1 **Breaking Free**
(Houston) Warner/Chappell Artemis Music Limited.

2 **Castle On A Cloud**
(Schönberg/Boublil/Natel/Kretzmer)
Alain Boublil Overseas Limited/SACEM.

3 **Chim Chim Cher-ee**
(Sherman/Sherman) Warner/Chappell Artemis Music Limited.

4 **Close Every Door**
(Lloyd Webber/Rice) The Really Useful Group Limited.

5 **Popular**
(Schwartlz) EMI Music Publishing Limited.

6 **I Whistle A Happy Tune**
(Hammerstein/Rodgers) EMI Music Publishing Limited.

7 **My Favourite Things**
(Hammerstein/Rodgers) EMI Music Publishing Limited.

8 **Sandy**
(St. Louis/Simon) Famous Music Publishing Limited.

9 **Where Is Love**
(Bart) Lakeview Music Publishing Company Limited.

10 **You're Never Fully Dressed Without A Smile**
(Charnin/Strouse) Chappell Morris Limited/
Warner/Chappell Music Limited.

To remove your CD from the plastic sleeve,
lift the small lip to break the perforations.
Replace the disc after use for convenient storage.